The Carving
on the Tree

The Carving on the Tree

by Elizabeth A. Campbell

Illustrated by William Bock

BOSTON   LITTLE, BROWN AND COMPANY   TORONTO

Books by Elizabeth A. Campbell

NAILS TO NICKELS
The Story of American Coins Old and New

FINS AND TAILS

THE CARVING ON THE TREE

LIBRARY OF CONGRESS CATALOG CARD NO. 67–21180

TR 00728 13 S2

LB 04683 33 E2

Fourth Printing

Acknowledgments

The author is grateful to the Historian of Fort Raleigh, Mrs. Louise Meekins, to Paul
Green, author of the play *The Lost Colony,* and to her husband for their encouragement and
assistance in making this book possible.

*Published simultaneously in Canada
by Little, Brown & Company (Canada) Limited*

PRINTED IN THE UNITED STATES OF AMERICA

For here once walked the men of dreams,
The sons of hope and pain and wonder,
Upon their foreheads truth's bright diadem,
The light of the sun in their countenance,
And their lips singing a new song —
A song for ages yet unborn,
For us the children that came after them —
"O new and mighty world to be!"
They sang,
"O land majestic, free, unbounded!"

This was the vision, this the fadeless dream —
Tread softly, softly now these yellow stricken sands.
This was the grail, the living light that leapt —
Speak gently, gently on these muted tongueless shores.

Now down the trackless hollow years
That swallowed them but not their song
We send response —
"O lusty singer, dreamer, pioneer,
Lord of the wilderness, the unafraid,
Tamer of darkness, fire and flood,
Of the soaring spirit winged aloft
On the plumes of agony and death —
Hear us, O hear!
The dream still lives,
It lives, it lives,
And shall not die!"

"The Dream," *by Paul Green*
from his play THE LOST COLONY

For
my sisters, Thelma and Ruth,
and
all my kith and kin,
especially
Mattie, Lois and Robert,
who shared their childhood with me

Contents

The Carving
on the Tree

Walter Raleigh's Dream

Walter Raleigh was a man who dreamed. He lived in England hundreds of years ago.

He dreamed of a faraway land across the ocean. That land was North America.

In other countries there were other men who dreamed of North America. Across the wide, wind-tossed ocean these explorers sailed in tiny sailing ships.

Many countries of Europe sent explorers to North America. They sailed up and down the seacoast, looking for places to start colonies and searching for treasures the new land might have.

Walter Raleigh wanted England to have a colony in the New World, too. This was his dream and greatest wish.

At that time the ruler of England was Queen Elizabeth I. She was Walter Raleigh's friend.

For a long time she had wished to have colonies in North America.

One day in the year 1584, Walter Raleigh asked his queen if he could send some explorers to the New World. She gave her permission.

It was the first step in making his dream come true.

First Voyage

Flowers were blooming and birds were singing in England. It was the month of April and spring was everywhere. Walter Raleigh was ready to send explorers to the New World. The Queen had given him land in Ireland and some tax money collected from the sale of wool and wine. Now he had money of his own with which to send explorers to North America.

On the 27th day of April, 1584, two small barks sailed out of the harbor of Plymouth,

England. They were outfitted by Walter Raleigh with men and supplies.

Raleigh told his captains, Philip Amados and Arthur Barlowe, to explore near the coast of the new land. They were to trade with the natives and find a good place for an English colony.

Queen Elizabeth would not let Raleigh go with his expedition. There was danger of war with Spain, and she needed his help.

The Englishmen took a Spanish navigator to guide them because he had sailed before to North America. The navigator was Simon Fer-

nando, a man to be feared in time to come.

Westward into the far-reaching ocean the small barks sailed. Only the winds and waves knew how long their journey would take.

Walter Raleigh and his friends watched from the harbor as long as the sails were in sight.

Would the men in the two small barks ever return?

Exploration

Sixty-nine days passed before land came into sight. The excited Englishmen watched and worked as Simon Fernando guided the barks.

They anchored at last in an inlet of shallow water and sandbars. In the distance there were low hills and green trees.

Climbing over the sides of the barks, they waded ashore into an unknown land.

The golden pebbles of the sandy beach crunched under the Englishmen's boots. Sea oats, clinging to the clumps of sand hills, waved a greeting in the hot July breeze.

The sailors watched as the sea gulls dropped large clams on the beach to break them open. The men ran to get the fresh seafood before the gulls could swoop down. Screaming in anger, the gulls soared over their heads.

When the explorers climbed to the nearest hill they saw more water to the west. It was the calm, quiet water of a sound. Now they knew that they were on a barrier island. This was a narrow outer island lying between the sea and the mainland.

The bushy red cedar trees shaded the men from the sun as they gathered grapes. Over the

sand hills and into the trees flowed the grape-
vines as far as they could see.

For two days the Englishmen explored the
narrow strip of land and found it full of small
animals and deer.

On the third day they saw boats in the distance. They knew that Indians lived in the New
World, so they were not surprised.

In boats of hollowed-out tree trunks, the Indians paddled across the sound. They wore garlands of snow goose feathers and skirts of animal skins.

Would they be friendly, or shoot their deadly arrows?

The explorers walked down to the beach to meet them. They held out pretty colored beads and little mirrors, while smiling at the strange men.

The Indians took the presents and passed them from one to another. They seemed pleased and began to spear and net fish. In a very short time they had many fish to lay before the Englishmen.

In this way they became friends and began to try to understand each other.

New World

As the days went by the Indians guided the white men up and down the outer islands. The explorers liked their guide Manteo. His tribe, which lived on Croatoan Island, was friendly and helpful.

One day an Indian named Wanchese took the explorers to visit his tribe on a small island in the sound. Here they found a village enclosed by a palisade. The chief made the explorers welcome to the island, Roanoke. This island was about six miles wide and twelve miles long.

Both captains and the sailors agreed that the island of Roanoke would be a fine place for a colony.

The Englishmen were delighted with the New World. Wherever they explored they claimed the land in the name of Queen Elizabeth of England.

Many tribes entertained them in their villages and traded with them. The tribal names were musical and strange: Cro a to ans, Ro an okes, Se co tans, Aq nos co qocs and Dasa mon que peucs.

One brave traded fifty animal skins for a copper kettle. One king traded twenty skins for a bright tin plate. He hung it around his neck on a string. Pointing with an arrow, he showed that it would make a fine shield.

Many women wore capes of snow goose feathers and had strings of pearls.

The Indians lived in such a land of plenty that they had time for dances and games.

One tribe had carved the tops of tree trunks to look like human heads. They set seven of these posts in a circle and danced around them.

The Indians showed the explorers how to plant maize, the grain we now call corn. They put a fish in each hole to help the maize grow faster.

The Englishmen watched the Indians smoke

a weed they called *uppowoc*. The weed was dried and stuffed in the bowl of a clay pipe. Simon Fernando explained that the weed was called tobacco by the Spanish.

After two months of exploration, the Englishmen decided they had better start home.

Manteo and Wanchese, who was also called Towaye, agreed to return to England with the explorers.

Their friends and families gathered on the sandy beaches to watch the strange boats with

white wings sail away. Would Manteo and Wanchese ever return?

Waving gaily to hide their fear, the Indians watched the barks go out of sight.

The Explorers Return

Before many months had passed the explorers reached England. Great excitement greeted the Englishmen, with their strange red men.

Why was smoke coming out of their noses and mouths? The clay pipes had to be touched and the tobacco tasted. Maize was passed from

hand to hand. Crowds gathered around Walter Raleigh, his explorers, and his Indians.

Raleigh was delighted with the success of his explorers. They had brought him a bracelet of pearls from the New World and the stories they told of the new land were wonderful to hear. The proud Wanchese and smiling Manteo were living proof of the friendly Indians.

But the explorers had not seen the outer banks of the New World in winter. They had not seen a storm lash Roanoke Island. They had not faced the frightening winds of a hurricane. They had not bled from the arrows of unfriendly Indians. Of these things they could not tell.

Queen Elizabeth was pleased with the report of the expedition. Wanchese and Manteo were a great attraction for her friends and visitors.

It was not long before she bestowed knighthood on Walter Raleigh, who thus became Sir Walter Raleigh.

The queen named the newly claimed land

Virginia, and planned an English colony there.

Now she was ready to help Sir Walter Raleigh by outfitting a ship with her own money.

First Colony of Men

By the next spring, Sir Walter Raleigh had a colony of men ready to sail. They were going to Roanoke Island in the new Virginia to build homes for others to follow.

Wanchese and Manteo must have been very anxious to start home. They had seen strange sights and eaten strange foods. They had many stories to tell their tribes.

Seven ships sailed out of the harbor at Plymouth, England, on April 9, 1585. The leader of the expedition was Sir Richard Grenville, a cousin of Sir Walter Raleigh.

In the first colony there were people with many trades, and many, many soldiers. There were carpenters, bricklayers, and weavers. An artist, John White, was sent to paint people and places in the New World. Another man, Thomas Hariot, was a writer and scientist who knew the names of plants and animals.

The captains of the first two ships returned with the group. Simon Fernando was again the navigator.

This expedition was made up of one hundred and eight men. Many dreamed of finding gold and silver, and owning land — one hundred and eight men, but no women to make the new Virginia colony seem like home.

The colonists stopped on the island of Puerto Rico in the West Indies. They needed to trade for animals and supplies.

The island was owned by the unfriendly country of Spain, so the men built a fort for protection while they were trading.

The carpenters built a pinnace — a small boat — which they loaded with horses, cows, goats, pigs, sheep, salt, sugar and many other supplies.

On June 26, 1585, the first colony landed on the outer island of Wokoken in the New World.

They sailed into the sound and on to Croatoan Island. Manteo's family rejoiced to see him. They helped the Englishmen fill their water casks and gave them fresh meat.

The men were anxious to reach Roanoke Island, so they sailed on through the inlet and up the sound.

The colonists had no sooner landed than Wanchese disappeared. He had seen enough of the English to last him a lifetime. They had a country of their own. Why did they want Roanoke Island too?

The men were too excited and busy to notice that Wanchese did not say farewell. Knowing that the Spanish did not want the English in the New World, they began to build a fort for protection.

The fort was a high wall of earth with a moat around it. The moat was a deep ditch too wide

to be jumped. Men could lie behind the wall and the earth would stop bullets or cannonballs that were fired into it.

Within the walls of the fort there was not enough room for houses. So they were built nearby of rough boards with roofs of marsh grasses and reeds.

The first colony in the new land of Virginia named their fort The New Fort in Virginia. They named their little village the "cittie of Ralegh."

Life in the First Colony

The Englishmen of the first colony had plenty of time to explore and to hunt for gold and silver.

Chief Wingina and his Indians on Roanoke Island planted crops of maize and made fish traps for the colonists.

The artist, John White, traveled into the villages, where he painted the homes, fields, boats,

From then on life in the first colony changed. Sir Richard took his ships back to England for supplies, and the Indians began open war.

When Wingina, the Roanoke Island Indian king, was killed in a battle, Wanchese became their enemy too. After that the Indians fought by destroying food, as well as with arrows.

The cornfields were stripped of corn and the fish traps destroyed. When the men went out to hunt they were in danger of an arrow in the back.

Now they realized how helpless they were, and how much the friendship of the Indians had meant.

By the time spring came the men were near starvation. They had eaten most of the animals they had brought with them. The others had been taken by the Indians or had run away.

At last they decided to divide into groups and go in different directions to find food.

One group paddled their dugout canoes to the outer sandy island across from Roanoke.

Every day they watched for the sails of the supply ships. They lived on fish, clams, oysters, and
whatever shellfish they could catch. Another
group went to Croatoan to find food and watch
for the ships.

There was no way to escape from this new

land of fear and starvation. The dugout canoes
and small pinnaces could not carry them back
to England, even if they had a navigator.

Where were Sir Richard Grenville and the
supply ships? Why didn't he come back?

The First Colony Gives Up

One sunny day in June, the men on one
outer island were beginning their daily work.

In the middle of the narrow island rose a
mountain of bare sand. From here they could
see Roanoke Island, as well as the sea. Each day
they climbed up the slippery sand mountain
and looked for ships. They had piled driftwood

ready to light in a giant bonfire if ships were sighted.

On this June day they reached the top of the mountain and looked toward the sea. Were those sails they saw? If so, were they English ships or Spanish ships?

If they were Spanish ships, perhaps the Spanish would take them prisoners. Wouldn't that be better than to die of starvation or an Indian arrow?

Quickly they lighted their bonfire. Slowly the damp driftwood sent columns of smoke into the sky.

The sails came nearer and the men fired the few rounds of powder they had saved.

The men left on Roanoke Island had seen

the smoke, so they paddled across the sound.

Closer and closer came the sails.

Soon the twenty-three English warships of Sir Francis Drake anchored offshore. The starving Englishmen were saved.

Governor Ralph Lane rowed out and went aboard to talk with Sir Francis. The sailors came ashore to exchange news and see the islands.

Sir Francis Drake offered the colonists a ship, two pinnaces and a number of small boats. He offered them supplies to last for a month. By that time the supply ships should be back from England.

Governor Lane did not want to give up the colony in Virginia. He and a few brave men like John White, the artist, were willing to accept Drake's kind offer.

But supplies and ships would not change the Indians into friends again. Even the hope of finding gold and silver in the new land could not make most of the men want to stay there any longer. They were hungry, frightened and homesick.

When Sir Francis Drake's ships sailed away on June 18, 1586, the first colony went with them. They abandoned the fort and the "cittie of Ralegh."

Two weeks later the supply ships came. Sir Richard Grenville hunted for the men of the first colony, but of course he could not find them.

Fifteen of his crew said that they would stay and hold the land for England while he went back for more colonists. The hope of finding pearls, gold and silver made them brave.

Sir Richard left the fifteen men enough supplies to last for two years, and sailed away.

The Indians watched from their hiding places in the marsh reeds.

Would these white men never give up? First there were two boats of men who were their friends. Then had come the many men with firesticks and armor who killed their king. Now there were only fifteen!

Soon Roanoke Island would belong to them again.

A Second Colony

Sir Walter Raleigh was deeply disappointed when his first colony came home. He did not have enough money left for ships and supplies to send another.

Finally he made a plan. He would organize a Virginia Company. The members of the company would share expenses. They would also share any wealth found in the New World.

Certain merchants and gentlemen were interested, so the Virginia Company was formed. Each member gave money to help outfit more ships.

John White, the artist who had wanted to stay in Virginia, was chosen to be the governor of the new colony. His daughter Eleanor and her husband Ananias Dare wanted to go and own land of their own.

Other men and a few women were willing to go too. They were people who knew about the raising of crops. Most of them were poor and wanted better homes for their families. Hadn't Sir Walter Raleigh promised at least five hundred acres to every man?

Before they sailed, it was decided that Roanoke Island was no longer a safe place.

Governor White remembered the tall pines and the blue waters of the Chesapeake Bay country farther north. He had explored there with the first colony and had drawn a map.

Sir Walter Raleigh gave the navigator, Simon Fernando, written orders, telling him to take this colony to the Chesapeake Bay land. On the way he was to pick up the fifteen men left by Sir Richard Grenville at Roanoke Island.

Ninety-one men, seventeen women, and nine boys sailed in three small ships from Plymouth, England. The number of sailors is not known.

This second colony knew something of the hardships and dangers which lay ahead. But the promise of land and the dreams of gold dimmed their fears.

Besides, they were going up the Chesapeake.

There the Indians might be their friends and teach them how to live in the new land.

Did tears fall as the seventeen women said good-bye to their friends and relatives?

Perhaps, but the new land of adventure called.

Long Voyage

On the voyages to the New World, the English ships had always stopped at the West Indies islands. The second colony stopped there too.

While the seasick ones rested, the others traded for supplies. The boys romped in the warm climate and ate the delicious fruits.

A small pinnace was built to carry the supplies. These colonists did not have money to buy the many animals and goods that the first colony had bought. There was no space to carry them, anyway.

Late in July of 1587 the ships reached the outer banks of North America. They passed by Croatoan Island and sailed north through the wide sound.

Governor White was anxious to pick up the

fifteen men at "the fort." There was a long way to sail to the Chesapeake Bay country. It was already too late to plant crops, but a fort and houses must be built before winter.

The ships anchored at the north end of Roanoke Island. Governor White prepared to take a small boat to pick up the men.

It was then that Simon Fernando spoke. "You will all disembark, here," he said. "I will guide you no farther. I want to return to England before winter."

Governor White and the startled colonists could not believe that he meant what he said. He had written orders to take them farther north. Roanoke Island was no longer a safe place.

In spite of their pleading, Fernando would not go farther. He ordered his sailors to unload the colonists and their supplies.

How terrified and discouraged they must have been!

Only the nine boys were cheerful. They were glad to disembark anywhere to stretch their legs and explore.

The sailors piled the colonists' supplies on the beach and turned the animals loose.

There was nothing for Governor White to do but guide his colony toward the fort. The women lifted their long skirts and trudged up the sandbanks into the tangle of grapevines.

Why hadn't Grenville's men come to meet them?

Where were the fifteen men?

The Fort

When the colonists reached the "cittie of Ralegh" there were no signs of life. The earthen
fort was torn down.

Vines covered the empty houses in the "cittie of Ralegh." Deer were eating the wild melons from vines that had crawled up the sides of

buildings. They scurried through the underbrush.

One lone skeleton greeted the frightened
people.

What should they do? They must have a
place for shelter, so first they must rebuild the
houses.

While some of the men worked to rebuild the
earthen fort, others worked on the houses. The
women and boys helped thatch the roofs. They
gathered marsh grasses and placed them in
layers as they had learned to do in England.

Governor White, with a few men, went to
Croatoan Island to visit Manteo's tribe. He
found them glad to see him, and he invited
them to come to the "cittie of Ralegh."

Manteo told Governor White that the Roanoke Island Indians had killed the fifteen men
in the fort.

When the men returned from their visit to
Croatoan they found that an Indian arrow had
killed one of the colonists, George Howe. He

had been crab fishing on the shore. Now little Georgie Howe was an orphan.

Governor White decided to act. Taking fifteen men, he slipped through the woods at night and attacked the Roanoke Indian village with fire and sword.

This was a terrible mistake. The unfriendly Roanoke Indians had abandoned their village.

Some Croatoan braves who were hunting had stopped in the empty village to look for corn. Governor White and his men had attacked Manteo's own friends and relatives.

Manteo explained the mistake to his tribe and Governor White expressed his deep sorrow.

The colonists could only hope that they were forgiven.

Christenings

The second week in August was a very special
one for the colonists.

Sir Walter Raleigh had asked that Manteo be
given a Christian name. A church service was
planned and Manteo's family invited.

The Roanoke Island Indians had moved to
the mainland, so the rector christened Manteo
the new Lord of Roanoke. This was to be his
Christian name. In this way the colonists tried
to thank Manteo for his friendship. This christening on August 13, 1587, was the first re-

corded Christian service by English Protestants in North America.

Five days after the christening of Manteo, Lord of Roanoke, there was another important event.

Governor White's granddaughter was born to Eleanor and Ananias Dare. The girl was the first child born in North America of English parents.

They christened this first baby of the colony Virginia, after the new land.

Soon after Virginia Dare was christened, the colonists held a meeting. They all agreed that someone should try to return to England for supplies. They feared that Simon Fernando would not tell the Virginia Company where he had left the colony.

Would Fernando take someone back? The ships were still in the sound. Was he waiting for them to become discouraged and beg to return? They had come too far to give up now.

Was he waiting to show Spanish warships

where the English colony was, so it could be destroyed?

Or was he only waiting for a good breeze to fill the sails?

No one knew. They could only guess.

Ships were needed to carry the colonists up the Chesapeake. They had only the small pinnace which they had built in the West Indies. Foods, tools, medicines, and gunpowder were needed, too.

"We need some wives," said one of the men. "Seventeen women cannot make homes and care for so large a colony."

So it was decided that Governor White should return to England if Simon would allow him to go.

"If we have to move while you are gone, we will carve a message on a tree," said Eleanor Dare.

"Carve a Maltese cross over the message if you are in distress," answered her father.

The colonists waited on the beach with fear

in their hearts as the governor rowed out to the ships to see Simon Fernando.

A swift west wind began to blow for the first time in weeks. While they watched, the sailors began to pull up the sails.

As Governor White climbed up the rope ladder to where Simon stood on deck, the sailors were pulling up the anchors.

The sails filled and the ships moved suddenly southward, toward the inlet to the sea. Governor White waved to the brave little group on the sandy beach.

Would Simon Fernando take him to England or throw him into the sea?

They could only wait and hope.

The Second Colony Waits and Hopes

Indian eyes had also watched the sails disappear. The Englishmen had killed their chief and taken their island. Had the ships gone back for more men?

The English firesticks were frightening and loud. But weren't the Indian arrows silent and deadly? Which was stronger?

The colonists busily prepared for winter. The women gathered white bayberries and boiled the wax into candles. The boys gathered yaupon leaves for tea. They gathered marsh grasses for bedding and driftwood for the fires.

After a few days of peaceful work, they were attacked. The Indians seemed to come from all directions.

Many of the colonists ran to the fort and lay on the ground. They realized then that something more than an earthen fort was needed.

When the attack was over, the frightened Englishmen buried their dead and the women tended their wounded.

The next job was to build a palisade around the "cittie." While some of the men stood guard, others sharpened tree trunks and set up the palisade.

Always as they worked, fear was with them.

Day after day the silent arrows hit their human targets.

When the men went to hunt for food, they found their animal traps gone and the fish traps destroyed. The deer had swum away from the noisy English guns long before. The ducks hid in the marsh grass or flew out of reach.

Soon winter hugged the little island. The

honking of the snow geese overhead was the
first sign.

The snow geese wintered on Croatoan Island,
home of Manteo's tribe. If only the friendly
tribe were near to help the colonists!

The windy arms of winter were not gentle.
They hugged the starving colonists with icy
fingers. The wild Atlantic Ocean pushed its

waters into the sound and the cold waves pounded the shore of the little island.

The clams dug deeper holes and hid from the colonists. The thin soup in the black iron pot had only mussels to flavor it now.

The nights were filled with flaming Indian arrows. Only a few houses had roofs that could keep out the rain.

With the cold, fear and hunger came disease and weakness.

One night the small group huddled around their campfire and discussed what could be done. There were those who believed that Simon Fernando did not take Governor White back to England. There were those who believed that the ships had been lost at sea and supplies would never come. Hadn't the governor promised to be back by Christmas?

Some believed that the Roanoke Island Indians only wanted their island back. They believed that if the Indians saw them leaving, they would let them go in peace.

Before Governor White left, the colony had discussed moving inland. The pinnace was still afloat. Should they start west toward the mainland? Or should they try to sail south to Croatoan Island, and hope for help from Manteo's people?

The little group was silent. They looked at Governor White's daughter for the answer.

Eleanor Dare's pale face glowed in the firelight. She held baby Virginia close to her body to keep her warm.

She had known for many days what her answer would be.

Eleanor Dare began to speak.

A Return for Supplies

Governor White reached England but he was greeted with sad news.

Spain had gathered her ships in a great fleet called the Spanish Armada. The king of Spain planned to go to war against England and destroy the Virginia colony in the New World.

Sir Walter Raleigh and Sir Richard Grenville had been supplying a fleet of ships. They were ready to send more colonists to Virginia when the war began.

As soon as the Spanish Armada anchored off the coast of England, all English ships were called to war. Sir Walter Raleigh's fleet was taken and turned into warships.

Queen Elizabeth could no longer dream of colonies in the New World. She must protect England first.

Governor White was greatly distressed. No

one knew how long the war with Spain would last. No one knew which country would win.

Sir Walter Raleigh and Governor White tried desperately to get supplies to the colonists.

At last Queen Elizabeth gave her permission for two small ships to try to slip by the Spanish Armada.

But even the tiny ships could not get through the war-torn sea. The last hope was lost.

A year passed and the Spanish Armada had been driven away, but Spain and England were still at war. Ships were not allowed to leave England.

Then Sir Walter Raleigh heard of a merchant who wanted to send ships to the West Indies to trade.

This was his chance. He told the merchant that he could get Queen Elizabeth's permission on one condition. The merchant's ships would have to take colonists and supplies to the Virginia colony.

The merchant agreed, and Sir Walter Raleigh got Queen Elizabeth's permission for him to sail. Governor White began gathering colonists together.

When the day for sailing came, the colonists and supplies were ready at the dock. The pigs squealed and the geese honked. The children jumped up and down in excitement.

Governor White was aboard one of the ships talking to the captain. Suddenly the sailors began to cast off and pull up the anchors. The sails were set and a breeze began tugging at them, as if anxious to start.

"Go home," the sailors yelled to the colonists. "The captains say there is no room for you."

The two ships sailed out of the harbor without the colonists or any supplies for the colony in Virginia.

Poor Governor White was alone. Would he ever reach Roanoke Island?

Governor White's Lonely Voyage

The two ships sailed to the West Indies, where they traded for months. Finally the captains agreed to take Governor White to Roanoke Island in Virginia before going back to England.

It was the month of August in 1590 when the ships reached the outer banks and the island of Croatoan. The ocean was wild and angry, stirred up by a hurricane. One of the ships was leaking. Governor White wondered whether Manteo and the Indians of Croatoan had forgiven him for attacking them by mistake three years before.

As the fresh water supply was low, the ships anchored near the wave-tossed beach. Captain Spicer and ten men from his ship lowered a boat and started toward Croatoan for water. Before they could reach the beach, the angry sea rolled over their boat. Only three of the men were saved.

Captain Cooke was the name of the second captain. He and his men were already afraid of the New World. After the accident they were terrified. The sailors wanted to turn back.

Governor White begged them to go on. "The sound will be calmer water," he encouraged.

Knowing that fresh water and meat were needed, Captain Cooke agreed to go on to Roanoke Island.

The sun had dropped behind the tall pines of the mainland when the ships reached Roanoke Island. A light appeared from shore. Smoke lifted white fingers as if to wave.

Captain Cooke decided to wait until morning before going ashore.

Governor White could hardly wait. He walked the deck and looked toward the island. Three years had passed since he had said farewell to the colony.

Return to Roanoke Island

The next morning was cloudy and windy. Governor White had never seen the waters of the sound so troubled. The little ships rocked against their anchors.

"Halloo!" called the sailors.

"Halloo!" mocked the sea gulls. They were the only welcoming sounds that came from Roanoke Island.

"Perhaps they think that we are Spanish ships," said Governor White. "Let's shout some English songs."

The sailors shouted English songs, blew the trumpet and fired a musket. Then they lowered the boats and went ashore.

Governor White and the Englishmen

climbed the banks through the tangled grape-
vines. They walked single file with their muskets ready.

In the distance a large tree attracted their at-
tention. As they drew nearer, they saw that
three letters had been cut into its bark. The
three letters were CRO.

Was it an unfinished word? Where was the
colony? The hope that Governor White had
held so long began to slip away. He began to
run, hacking at the twisted vines with his
sword.

Ahead of them was a palisade. It was made like those around the Indian villages that Governor White had once visited. The palisade was around the "cittie of Ralegh."

As the little band of Englishmen came to the gate they stopped. Carefully, with muskets raised, they crept forward.

There were no shouts of welcome. There were no Indian war whoops either. The sailors lowered their guns, for an empty village lay before them. Even the houses were gone. The growth of the underbrush showed that seasons had passed since anyone had lived there.

While some of the men looked along the shore for signs of the pinnace, others searched the island.

Governor White looked around the fort. Where the "cittie" had been he found rusted tools. There was a deep trench where chests of belongings had been hidden. There he found his own three chests.

The chests had been broken open and the contents scattered about. His books had been torn from their covers and were decaying in the weeds. His maps were rain-soaked and ruined. His suit of armor was full of holes caused by rust.

There were no skeletons or signs of battle.

Suddenly one of the sailors yelled, "Look!" He pointed to one of the posts in the palisade.

Everyone ran to the post. The bark of the tree trunk had been peeled back and a word carved on the wood.

The Roman letters were clear. They did not look as if they had been carved in a hurry.

The word was CROATOAN.

"God be praised!" said Governor White. "There is no Maltese cross above the message. They did not leave in distress. They have gone to the island of Croatoan where Manteo's tribe could help them. We need search no longer. Let us hurry back to Croatoan."

Despair

"Croatoan!" whispered the sailors. "The sea is full of demons there. They have swallowed seven men. We will not stop again."

Governor White sat on the sandy shore with his head in his hands. Some of the sailors gath-

ered wild grapes and melons. Others fished and
dug clams from the shallow sound.

As the afternoon wore on the clouds gathered, and the sky became dark. The waters of
the sound grew rougher and rougher.

The sailors filled the water casks and started

back to the anchored ships. Before they had gone far, the waves threatened to swamp the tiny boats. In order to save themselves the men rolled the heavy water casks overboard. Now their water supply was dangerously low.

By morning the anchor cable of one ship had

broken. Both anchor and cable slipped into the water and were lost. The ships had left England with four anchors and four cables. Now only one of each was left.

Captain Cooke decided to set sail with no landings until they reached the West Indies. He promised Governor White that he would bring him back to Croatoan in the spring.

As they passed through the inlet near Croatoan, Governor White begged the captain to try to anchor so that he could go ashore.

He was near and yet so far from Croatoan. He was near and yet so far because the sailors would not lower the sails or anchor. The ships passed through the storm-tossed inlet into an angry ocean.

England Forever

The winds of the Atlantic Ocean had plans of their own for Governor White and the two ships. They blew the ships off course so that they never reached the West Indies. After many months, the battered and leaking ships reached England.

The merchants of the Virginia Company would not agree to send more colonists or to search for the lost colony.

Governor White did not have enough money to buy or supply a ship of his own. The sad old man's last written words were, "I would to God my wealth were answerable to my will."

Sir Walter Raleigh still thought of the Virginia Colony as his own. As soon as he could raise the money to supply a ship, he sent an expedition to hunt for the colonists.

During the next twelve years he sent out five expeditions. It was said that he spent over forty thousand pounds of his own money. Each time the men came back with different tales and excuses, but no news of the colonists.

Sir Walter never really knew whether these expeditions hunted for the lost colony or not. His last expedition came back in 1602, saying that bad weather had kept them from searching.

In 1603 Queen Elizabeth died and King James I became king of England.

King James imprisoned Sir Walter Raleigh in the Tower of London. He had suspected Sir Walter of plotting to make someone else the new ruler.

During his imprisonment, Sir Walter heard of a new colony being sent to the New World. They were going up the Chesapeake Bay in Virginia where the lost colony had planned to go.

With a final hope of finding his lost colony, Sir Walter Raleigh begged King James to let him go too.

King James refused his request. A few years later, the king ordered him beheaded.

Sir Walter Raleigh never saw the "faire land" of Virginia. But he did live long enough to know that his dream had come true. The colony that went up the Chesapeake had been living in Virginia for nine years before Sir Walter died.

This was the Jamestown colony, the first permanent English colony in the New World of North America.

The Lost Colony

What could have happened to the lost colony?

Some historians believe that the people could have been massacred by the unfriendly Roanoke Indians on their way to Croatoan Island. There were no skeletons or signs of battle at the fort on Roanoke Island when Governor White hunted for them.

Some think that they could have been carried away and killed by Spaniards. Spain was at war with England and did not want an English colony in the New World.

There are many who like to believe that the colony lived to reach Croatoan and the friendly tribe of Manteo. One hundred years later there were gray-eyed Indians in the Croatoan tribe. They said their ancestors were white men who could "talk in a book." Many of them had the same last names as the lost colonists.

A friendly Indian told the Jamestown colonists that he knew of palefaces who once lived on the mainland farther south. He said that Chief

Powhatan's tribe killed all but four men, two boys, and one young maid.

Today Roanoke Island, North Carolina, where Virginia Dare was born, is mysteriously beautiful. It is tied to the outer islands and the mainland by two ribbons of bridges. Quietly it sits in winter wind and summer sun, waiting in the sound. Southward curves a fringe of sand-colored marsh grass. It ruffles around the shore like the fancy collars of Walter Raleigh's day.

To the north, toward the fort, the banks rise steeply from the sandy beaches. Wild grape-vines cling to the steep banks as they did when the colonists lived there. Wind-twisted trees of cedar, holly, dogwood and pine lean away from the sea.

The sea oats wave, and the sea gulls scream as they drop clams to the pebbles on the beaches.

The wild bayberry bushes grow without coaxing. There are no colonists to gather their white, waxy berries for candles.

The yaupon bushes grow their clusters of tiny red berries. There are no Indians to boil their leaves into medicine tea.

Many roads are of sand and the names of Manteo and Wanchese are spoken daily, because they are the names of the two villages.

Every fall the snow geese fly over the little island. They spend the winter a few miles south on the outer islands. Manteo's tribe is not there to ask for their feathers and they live in peace.

Through the years the wind and waves have opened and closed inlets. They have pushed some of the outer islands together. Now there is no Croatoan. Today the outer-banks islands of North Carolina that the lost colonists knew are named Hatteras and Ocracoke.

What happened to the lost colony, over three hundred years ago?

The Names of the Lost Colonists

Morris Allen
Arnold Archard
Joyce Archard
Richard Arthur

Roger Bailie
Mark Bennet
William Berde
Henry Berrye
Richard Berrye
Michael Bishop
John Borden
John Bridger
John Bright
John Brooke
Henry Browne
William Browne
John Burden
Thomas Butler

Anthony Cage
Alis Chapman
John Chapman
John Cheven
William Clement
Dame Colman
Thomas Colman

Christopher Cooper
John Cotsmur

Ananias Dare
Eleanor Dare
Richard Darige
Henry Dorrell
William Dutton

John Earnest
Thomas Ellis
Edmond English

John Farre
Charles Florrie

John Gibbs
Elizabeth Gland
Thomas Gramme

Thomas Harris
Thomas Harris
Dyonis Harvie
Margery Harvie
John Hemmington
Thomas Hewet
James Hynde

Henry Johnson
Nicholas Johnson
Griffen Jones
Jane Jones
John Jones

Richard Kemme

James Lasie
Margaret Lawrence
Peter Little
Robert Little
William Lucas

Jane Mannering
George Martyn
Emma Merrimoth
Michael Myllet
Henry Mylton

Humfrey Newton
William Nicholes

Hugh Pattenson
Henry Payne
Rose Payne
Thomas Phevens

Jane Pierce
Edward Powell
Wenefrid Powell
Roger Prat

Henry Rufoote

John Sampson
Thomas Scot
Richard Shaberdge
Thomas Smith
William Sole
John Spendlove
John Starte

Thomas Stevens
John Stilman
Martyn Sutton

Audrey Tappan
Richard Taverner
Hugh Tayler
Clement Taylor
Richard Tompkins
Thomas Topan
John Tydway

Ambrose Vickers
Elizabeth Vickers

Thomas Warner
Joan Warren
William Waters
Cuthbert White
Richard Wildye
Robert Wilkinson
William Willes
Agnes Wood
Lewes Wotton
John Wright
Brian Wyles
John Wyles

BABIES BORN IN VIRGINIA

Virginia Dare ——— Harvie

CHILDREN WHO WERE WITH THE LOST COLONISTS

Thomas Archard
Robert Ellis
George Howe

Thomas Humfrey
John Prat
John Sampson

Thomas Smart
Ambrose Vickers
William Wythers

INDIANS THAT WERE IN ENGLAND AND RETURNED HOME TO VIRGINIA WITH THEM

Manteo   Towaye (Wanchese)